C O N T E N T S

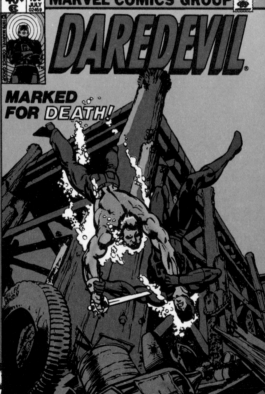

STAN LEE PRESENTS: ™

DAREDEVIL

IN

"MARKED FOR DEATH"

C R E D I T S

ROGER McKENZIE
writer

FRANK MILLER
penciler

KLAUS JANSON
inker

AL MILGROM
and
MARY JO DUFFY
original editors

RALPH MACCHIO
reprint editor

TOM DeFALCO
editor in chief

JOHN ROMITA JR. *and* AL WILLIAMSON *cover artists*

DAREDEVIL®: Marked for Death. ™ Originally published in magazine form as DAREDEVIL #s 159, 160, 161, 163, 164. Published by Marvel Comics, 387 Park Avenue South, New York, N.Y. 10016. Copyright © 1979, 1980, 1990 by Marvel Entertainment Group, Inc. All rights reserved. DAREDEVIL, "Marked for Death" and all prominent characters appearing herein and the distinctive likenesses thereof, are trademarks of Marvel Entertainment Group, Inc. No part of this book may be printed or reproduced in any manner whatsoever whether mechanical or electronic, without written permission of the publisher.

Printed in the UNITED STATES OF AMERICA

First Printing: March 1990

ISBN# 0-87135-634-1

He dwells in eternal night—but the blackness is filled with sounds and scents other men cannot perceive. Though attorney MATT MURDOCK is *blind*, his other senses function with *superhuman sharpness*—his *radar sense* guides him over every obstacle! He stalks the streets by night, a red-garbed foe of evil!

STAN LEE PRESENTS: DAREDEVIL, THE MAN WITHOUT FEAR!®

PROLOGUE--

"GENTLEMEN, IF WE ARE ALL PRESENT, SHALL WE GET DOWN TO BUSINESS?"

BOWLING FOR BUCKS

"BEFORE WE DISCUSS THE FINAL TERMS OF OUR CONTRACT, I'D LIKE YOU TO STUDY THIS FILM-CLIP CAREFULLY."

"HERE IS YOUR TARGET. AS YOU UNDOUBTEDLY KNOW, HIS NAME IS DAREDEVIL, ALTHOUGH HE IS OFTEN CALLED THE MAN WITHOUT FEAR."

"I WANT YOU TO TRACK HIM DOWN. I DON'T CARE HOW YOU DO IT-- AND WHEN YOU HAVE FOUND HIM I WANT HIM--"

ESPECIALLY MURDER, MR. SLAUGHTER. YOU KNOW THAT AS WELL AS I.

THAT'S WHY YOU ARE HERE. I WANT THE BEST THAT MONEY CAN BUY.

I AM PREPARED TO PAY TWO-HUNDRED-THOUSAND NOW, AS A TOKEN OF MY SINCERITY--

--AND AN *ADDITIONAL* THREE-HUNDRED-THOU-SAND IF YOU BRING ME DAREDEVIL'S BODY, OR CONCLUSIVE PROOF OF HIS DEATH, WITHIN FORTY-EIGHT HOURS.

HALF A MILLION DOLLARS...

DONE, MR. PONDEXTER.

6

MURDER!

CAN YOU DO IT?

ANYTHING IS POSSIBLE, FOR A PRICE...

...EVEN MURDER.

ROGER McKENZIE: WRITER
FRANK MILLER: PENCILER
KLAUS JANSON: INKER
JIM NOVAK: LETTERER
GLYNIS WEIN: COLORIST
MARY JO DUFFY
ALLEN MILGROM } EDITORS
JIM SHOOTER: ED.-IN-CHIEF

YOU MUST HATE THIS DAREDEVIL VERY MUCH.

KLIK

REWIND
PLAY
STOP
FAST

SNAK
SNAK
SNAK
SNAK

YES...

THE FOLLOWING AFTERNOON...

I'M SORRY, YOU'LL HAVE TO ASK DAREDEVIL ABOUT THAT!

AND SO, CONTROVERSY CONTINUES TO CENTER AROUND MATTHEW MURDOCK, ONE OF THE NATION'S BEST KNOWN AND MOST RESPECTED PUBLIC DEFENDERS--

-- WHO WAS ALLEGEDLY THE VICTIM OF A BIZARRE KIDNAPPING LATE LAST NIGHT, THAT LED TO THE DEATHS OF THREE MEN IN A SMALL, UPTOWN CEMETERY! *

I'VE NO COMMENT FOR THE PRESS AT THIS TIME!

BUT, COUNSELOR--

*SEE DD #158 FOR DETAILS --AL.

YOU HEARD MY PARTNER-- NO COMMENT!

IT'S WHAT WE DIDN'T HEAR THAT INTERESTS ME!

BEN URICH TAKES A FINAL DRAG ON HIS CIGARETTE. THE VETERAN REPORTER DOESN'T REALIZE IT YET, BUT HE'S JUST EMBARKED ON WHAT WILL PROVE TO BE THE MOST ASTOUNDING STORY OF HIS CAREER...

THERE'S MORE TO MATT MURDOCK THAN MEETS THE EYE-- I'D BET MY PRESS CARD ON IT!

YOU'RE LATE, COUNSELOR! ENJOYING YOUR SUDDEN NOTORIETY?

THAT'S HIM, LEACH, THE BLIND GUY! TELL MR. SLAUGHTER EVERYTHING'S GOING ACCORDING TO PLAN!

YOUR HONOR, WITH THE COURT'S INDULGENCE--

--AND ON BEHALF OF MY CLIENT, I MOVE FOR A TEMPORARY POSTPONEMENT OF THIS HEARING.

YOUR HONOR, AT THIS LATE DATE THIS IS MOST UNUSUAL.

THESE ARE MOST UNUSUAL CIRCUMSTANCES, YOUR HONOR.

JUST OUR LUCK TO GET JUDGE COFFIN... HE'S TOUGH AS NAILS!

GENTLEMEN, IT IS THE SOLE CONCERN OF THIS COURT TO SEE THAT JUSTICE IS SERVED. THEREFORE, I WILL GRANT YOU YOUR EXTENSION, COUNSELOR. YOU MAY HAVE ONE WEEK...

...BUT I DO NOT LIKE IT, MURDOCK, AND I DO NOT LIKE YOU!

THE GUILTY MUST PAY FOR THEIR CRIMES, AND BY GOD, SO LONG AS I AM JUDGE THEY WILL! ONE WAY...OR ANOTHER...

LATER, NEAR THE STOREFRONT, FREE LEGAL CLINIC OF NELSON AND MURDOCK...

--AND KEEP THE CHANGE!

THEY'RE HERE!

LET'S GET THIS OVER WITH!

CHIKK

TAP TAP

"THEY'RE HERE?" "LET'S GET THIS OVER WITH?"

WHAT'S WRONG? YOU'RE JUMPY AS A FROG!

IT'S PROBABLY NOTHING, FOGGY. I JUST THOUGHT I ...HEARD SOMETHING...

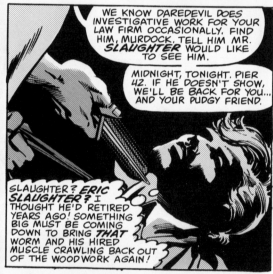

MIDNIGHT. THE WITCHING HOUR. BUT IT ISN'T A WITCH THAT PROWLS HELL'S KITCHEN THIS NIGHT.

IT IS A DEVIL...

...A GRIM AND *SIGHTLESS* DEVIL THAT GLIDES AS SILENTLY AS A MOONCAST SHADOW ACROSS DARK ROOFTOPS...

...AND DOWN DIRTY, CHEERLESS BACKSTREETS TOWARD THE FOG-SHROUDED WATERS OF THE HUDSON RIVER AND...

PIER 42--! I'LL GIVE SLAUGHTER CREDIT, HE COULDN'T HAVE CHOSEN A LONLIER OR MORE FOREBODING LOCALE!

IT'S THE PERFECT SPOT FOR A MURDER!

PAUSE NOW WITH DAREDEVIL, CROUCHED IN THE SHADOWS OF AN OLD, FIRE-GUTTED BROWNSTONE OVERLOOKING THE WATERFRONT. CLOSE YOUR EYES AND LISTEN TO THE MUTED SOUNDS OF THE HARBOR AT NIGHT...

...TO DISTANT SHIPS MOURNING FITFULLY, LOST SOMEWHERE IN THE DARKNESS AND THE FOG...

...TO THE RELENTLESS SLAP OF BLACK, BRINY WATER AGAINST ROUGH-HEWN WOODEN PILINGS AS A LONELY FIGURE PACES SLOWLY BACK AND FORTH ALONG PIER 42.

ALL THIS DAREDEVIL HEARS...

...AND MORE!

HE'S LATE!

SNK

KLEK

ALL THIS HE SENSES...

...AND MORE BESIDES!

THE UNMISTAKABLE SCENT OF BURNING TOBACCO--

...AND FAINTER, THE BITTER SMELL OF CORDITE AND GUN-POWDER!

WHERE IS HE?

THIS DOESN'T MAKE SENSE. SLAUGHTER IS AN OLD MAN, SO WHY RISK COMING OUT OF RETIREMENT JUST TO PUT A CONTRACT OUT ON ME?

WHERE'S THE PROFIT IN THAT?

THEN AGAIN, SLAUGHTER *COULD* BE WORKING FOR SOMEBODY ELSE. IT'S POSSIBLE, IF THE PRICE WAS RIGHT.

I DON'T LIKE THIS! I DON'T LIKE IT ONE BIT! WHAT IF SOMETHING GOES WRONG?

WHAT *CAN* GO WRONG? WE'RE THE BEST THAT MONEY CAN BUY... AND WHAT WE *DO* BEST IS KILLIN'!

NOTHIN' THAT WALKS, CRAWLS OR FLIES IS GONNA GET PAST US...

...IN ONE PIECE...

HEY! I THOUGHT I HEARD SOMETHIN'!

WELL, I DON'T SEE NOTHIN'!

PSSTT... FIVER! WHAT ABOUT YOU? SEE ANYTHING YET?

IN *THIS* PEA-SOUP? YOU GOT TO BE KIDDIN'!

KATHAK

WHAT THE--?

KRAK

13

IT'S HIM! DAREDEVIL!

WHUFF--!

ALL RIGHT, CLOWNS, I WANT SOME ANSWERS --AND I WANT THEM FAST!

TANG

MR. SLAUGHTER SAID YOU HAD TO DIE! THAT'S ALL *YOU* NEED TO KNOW!

THERE THEY ARE! CAREFUL, YOU'LL HIT LEECH!

SO? I NEVER LIKED THE CREEP ANYWAY!

BLAM BLAM

BLAM

14

VIIP

VIIP

VIIP

THE DARK, BULLET-RIDDLED RIVER IS COLD. AS COLD AS A TOMB.

BUT NOT AS COLD AS THE LIFELESS HANDS THAT CLUTCH THE MAN WITHOUT FEAR IN A DESPERATE DEATH-GRIP...

...DRAGGING HIM DOWN INTO A WATERY WORLD...

...WHERE LIFE IS MEASURED *NOT* IN YEARS AND DAYS...

...BUT RATHER IN MINUTES...

....AND SECONDS!

AND EITHER A MAN IS QUICK, OR SURELY HE IS--

16

H-HE KNOWS WHAT WE'RE GONNA DO EVEN B-BEFORE WE DO IT! L-LIKE HE CAN READ OUR M-MINDS OR SOMETHIN'!

NO, I CAN'T! BUT I CAN HEAR YOUR HEARTBEATS... SENSE YOUR SLIGHTEST MOVEMENTS! *I* MAY BE BLIND, BUT *YOU* ARE THE ONES WHO CAN-NOT SEE!

THAT TAKES CARE OF YOUR PARTNERS, 'TURK', EXCEPT FOR THE DECOY ON THE PIER... AND HE CAN'T HELP YOU NOW!

I WANT ANSWERS, TURK!

N-NO--!

S-STAY AWAY FROM ME, DEVIL! I GOT MY O-ORDERS--

CHUDD

BLAM

MY EARS!

SUPER-SENSITIVE EARS. EARS THAT CAN NORMALLY HEAR THE FAINTEST WHISPER A BLOCK AWAY...

BUT NOW DAREDEVIL CAN'T EVEN HEAR HIMSELF SCREAMING IN AGONY...

NNNOOOO!

...HE CAN'T HEAR ANYTHING, AS A MATTER OF FACT...

HEY! THE SHOOTIN'S STOPPED!

TURK? FIVER? LEACH? DID YOU GET HIM?

WHAT'S WITH YOU GUYS, ANYWAY? ANSWER ME! DID YOU--?

Y-YOU.

W-WON'T *ANYTHING* STOP YOU?

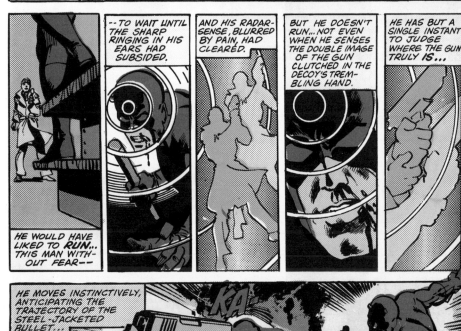

HE WOULD HAVE LIKED TO *RUN*... THIS MAN WITH-OUT FEAR--

--TO WAIT UNTIL THE SHARP RINGING IN HIS EARS HAD SUBSIDED.

AND HIS RADAR-SENSE, BLURRED BY PAIN, HAD CLEARED.

BUT HE DOESN'T RUN... NOT EVEN WHEN HE SENSES THE DOUBLE IMAGE OF THE GUN CLUTCHED IN THE DECOY'S TREMBLING HAND.

HE HAS BUT A *SINGLE* INSTANT TO JUDGE WHERE THE GUN TRULY *IS*...

...AND IF HE HAS CHOSEN WRONG, HE HAS CHOSEN DEATH.

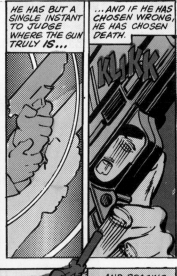

KLIKK

HE MOVES INSTINCTIVELY, ANTICIPATING THE TRAJECTORY OF THE STEEL-JACKETED BULLET...

KA

BLAM

...AND BRACING FOR THE JOLTING AND POSSIBLY FATAL IMPACT...

...BUT HE *NEVER* RUNS.

He dwells in eternal night—but the blackness is filled with sounds and scents other men cannot perceive. Though attorney MATT MURDOCK is *blind*, his other senses function with *superhuman sharpness*—his *radar sense* guides him over every obstacle! He stalks the streets by night, a red-garbed foe of evil!

Stan Lee PRESENTS: **DAREDEVIL,** THE MAN WITHOUT FEAR! ®

EPILOGUE--

IT'S AT TIMES LIKE THIS THAT SHE NEEDS TO BE ALONE IN THE QUIET SECLUSION OF HER POSH PENTHOUSE APARTMENT IN NEW YORK'S FASHIONABLE WALDORF TOWERS...

THE CURSE IS ON THE WIDOW.

...TO LET HER HAIR DOWN AND TRY TO FORGET THAT SOONER OR LATER THE BLACK WIDOW BRINGS *DEATH* TO EVERYONE SHE TOUCHES...

YES, THE CURSE IS ON THE WIDOW... AND IT HAS COME FULL CIRCLE...

GOOD EVENING, NATASHA ROMANOFF.

SHE HAS FELT IT GATHERING FOR HOURS NOW, A VAGUE *UNEASINESS* AS THREATENING AS THE HEAVY STORM CLOUDS THAT DARKEN THE SKIES ABOVE HER.

A LOVELY NIGHT FOR MURDER, ISN'T IT?

BULLSEYE?!

I'LL BREAK YOU, WIDOW, JUST AS EASILY AS I SHATTERED THAT MIRROR!

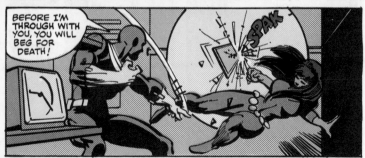

BEFORE I'M THROUGH WITH YOU, YOU WILL BEG FOR DEATH!

YOU WILL RUN--

--PERHAPS EVEN TRY TO FIGHT, AT FIRST!

BUT IT WILL DO YOU NO GOOD--

--BECAUSE IN MY HANDS ANYTHING AND *EVERYTHING* IS A DEADLY WEAPON!

EVEN YOU, WIDOW!

ESPECIALLY YOU!

YOU WILL BE THE INSTRUMENT OF *DAREDEVIL'S* DEATH! WHEN HE LEARNS I HAVE *YOU,* HE WILL COME FOR *ME*--

--AND THAT IS WHEN I WILL *KILL* YOU BOTH!

KRAKK

NO!

THAKK

NO!

NO!

SPAKK

SNIK

...BUT THERE'S AS NO ONE ALIVE AS RESOURCEFUL AS BULLSEYE!

YOU'RE... RESOURCEFUL, WIDOW... I'LL... GIVE YOU THAT...

25

SPLAMM

KARSSH

NO ONE!

NOW, WIDOW, WE WAIT!

SKLEKK

I, FOR REVENGE...

...YOU...AND DAREDEVIL, THE MAN YOU LOVE... FOR DEATH!

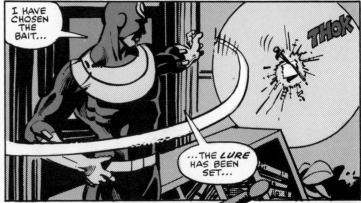

I HAVE CHOSEN THE BAIT...

THOK

...THE LURE HAS BEEN SET...

...AND SOON THE TRAP WILL BE SPRUNG!

26

IN THE HANDS OF BULLSEYE

BY MID-MORNING OF THE FOLLOWING DAY THE RAIN HAS BECOME A STEADY DOWNPOUR...

MATT, I DON'T SEE WHY I HAD TO COME HERE, NOT TODAY...

...AND NOT WITH *THEM!*

ROGER MCKENZIE
SCRIPT

FRANK MILLER & KLAUS JANSON
PENCILS   INKS

JOE ROSEN, LETTERING GLYNIS WEIN, COLORING
MARY JO DUFFY AND ALLEN MILGROM
EDITORS

JIM SHOOTER EDITOR-IN-CHIEF

27

THEY'RE...WE'RE...HERE BECAUSE WE CARE ABOUT YOU, HEATHER, AND WE THINK ITS TIME YOU FACED THE TRUTH!

THE TRUTH? DO YOU HONESTLY THINK I DON'T KNOW THE TRUTH?

MY FATHER IS DEAD...

HEATHER, KNOWING THE TRUTH AND LEARNING TO ACCEPT IT ARE TWO DIFFERENT THINGS. IF WE HADN'T BROUGHT YOU HERE...

...MAYBE I'D NEVER HAVE COME? IS THAT SUCH A BAD THING MATT? I'VE LOST MY FATHER AND EVERYONE WHO--!

ACHOO

NOT EVERYONE, DARLING...

HAVEN'T I, MATT?

WHEN I...WHEN MY FATHER...NEEDED YOU MOST, YOU WERE ALWAYS TOO BUSY PLAYING DAREDEVIL TO HELP US.

PLEASE, MATT, PROMISE ME YOU WON'T EVER LET THAT HAPPEN AGAIN.

MATT...?

WHY DON'T YOU ANSWER ME?

HONESTLY, MATTHEW MURDOCK, YOU'RE THE MOST STUBBORN MAN I'VE EVER KNOWN! JUST WHAT IS IT YOU'RE TRYING TO PROVE?

I'M NOT TRYING TO PROVE ANYTHING. I CAN'T HELP *WHAT* I AM, AND I CAN'T CHANGE *WHO* I AM.

I HAVE CERTAIN RESPONSIBILITIES THAT--!

SMAK

MR. MURDOCK, AS FAR AS I'M CONCERNED-- YOU CAN TAKE YOUR RESPONSIBILITIES AND--!

MATT? HE NEEDS US, FOGGY!

EASY, BECKY. I'M NOT SURE WHAT JUST HAPPENED, BUT I DO KNOW MY PARTNER, AND RIGHT NOW...

... I THINK HE'D RATHER BE ALONE...

I HATE BEING ALONE... • • •

I WISH HEATHER AND I COULD HAVE BEEN MORE LIKE *THAT* COUPLE.

THEY DON'T SEEM TO HAVE A CARE IN THE WORLD.

I CAN'T BLAME HEATHER FOR BEING BITTER, BUT SHE *IS* WRONG ABOUT ONE THING. I DON'T LIVE UNDER THE SHADOW OF DAREDEVIL.

IF ANYTHING, I LIVE UNDER THE SHADOW OF THE PROMISE I MADE MY FATHER YEARS AGO.

I SWORE TO HIM I'D MAKE SOMETHING OF MYSELF, AND I THINK I'VE SUCCEEDED... BOTH AS MATT MURDOCK...

...AND AS DAREDEVIL...

BUT SOMETIMES I JUST GET SO BLAMED LONELY... I NEED SOMEBODY TO TALK TO.

SOMEONE WHO CAN UNDERSTAND WHAT I'M GOING THROUGH.

SOMEONE LIKE... NATASHA.

I HAVEN'T SEEN HER IN SEVERAL DAYS...

TAK

...I GUESS SHE'S BEEN TIED UP.

BUT I HOPE SHE'S NOT *TOO* BUSY TO SPARE A FEW MINUTES FOR AN OLD FRIEND.

WITH PRACTICED EASE, THE SIGHTLESS MAN WITHOUT FEAR SPRINTS UP A SHADOWED FLIGHT OF STAIRS THAT LEADS TO THE RAIN-SPLATTERED ROOFTOP OF HIS UPPER EAST-SIDE BROWNSTONE--AND TO AN OLD, SEEMINGLY DECREPIT SKYLIGHT.

HIS FOOT STABS AT A CONCEALED SWITCH...

...AND SENSING HE IS UNOB-SERVED...

SKREEK

KOAK

O-OH, MY--!

HE SPEEDS ACROSS MANHATTAN THROUGH THE DARKNESS AND THE RAIN TO...

NATASHA, IT'S MATT! I SENSED YOUR WINDOW WAS OPEN, I HOPE I'M NOT INTRUD--!

NATASHA?

SHE DOES NOT ANSWER...

...AND HIS UNIQUE RADAR-SENSE QUICKLY CONFIRMS WHAT HE HAD ALREADY BEGUN TO SUSPECT. SOMETHING IS WRONG.

SOMETHING IS VERY, VERY WRONG. HER APARTMENT IS A SHAMBLES.

HE DETECTS THE UNMISTAKABLE ODOR OF DRIED **BLOOD** CAKED ON THE BASE OF A HEAVY CERAMIC VASE.

AND THEN...

FLAP FLIP

EH--?

HIS SUPER-SENSITIVE FINGERS TREMBLE AS THEY SCAN THE SURFACE OF THE WIND-BLOWN NOTE...

NATASHA!

LATER, AT THE DAILY BUGLE...

OH, NO! NOT *ANOTHER* SPIDER-MAN EXPOSE!

...JUST WHAT INFORMATION *DO* YOU HAVE ON BULLSEYE?

NOTHING WE DIDN'T PRINT, DAREDEVIL. HIS ESCAPE WAS FRONT PAGE NEWS. I'M SURPRISED YOU DIDN'T HEAR ABOUT IT.

I'VE BEEN BUSY LATELY. COULD YOU FILL ME IN? IT'S VERY IMPORTANT!

I'LL BE GLAD TO... *IF* YOU TELL ME HOW LONG YOU'VE KNOWN MATT MURDOCK.

A WHILE. NOW, ABOUT BULLSEYE...

WELL...

HARD WORK

EVER HURT ANYBODY

PRIOR TO HIS ARRAIGNMENT ON SIX COUNTS OF ATTEMPTED MURDER, HE WAS TAKEN TO BELLEVUE FOR PSYCHIATRIC OBSERVATION.

ACCORDING TO OUR SOURCES HE WAS A MODEL PRISONER--

"--UNTIL FOUR DAYS AGO!"

...AND YOU SAY YOUR FATHER *BEAT* YOU?

YES, UNTIL I WAS FOURTEEN.

HMMM, I SEE. AND WHAT HAPPENED THEN?

I KILLED HIM.

"BEFORE ANY-ONE COULD STOP HIM, HE TOOK A NURSE AS HOSTAGE..."

STEP AWAY FROM THAT DOOR MISTER! *NOW!*

S-SURE... JUST T-TAKE IT EASY...

EXIT

"...AND BLASTED HIS WAY TO FREEDOM!"

"HE FLED IN A STOLEN POLICE CRUISER THAT WAS LATER FOUND ABANDONED IN QUEENS--

"--AND BY NOW HE'S PROBABLY LONG--

--GONE...

BEN URICH STUDIES THE OPEN WINDOW FOR SEVERAL MINUTES BEFORE CROSSING THE BUSTLING NEWSROOM...

...TO REMOVE *ANOTHER* FOLDER FROM HIS FILES.

A FOLDER THAT HE HAS CAREFULLY CROSS-INDEXED UNDER 'M'...

...AS IN MURDOCK...

LATER, JUST OFF SOUTH STREET, IN THE COLD, RAIN-DRENCHED SHADOWS OF THE BROOKLYN BRIDGE...

IT'S ALL TOO CLEAR NOW. BULLSEYE MUST HAVE HIRED ERIC SLAUGHTER AND HIS GOONS TO KILL ME.* WHEN THEY FAILED, HE WENT AFTER NATASHA.

BUT SHE MEANS NOTHING TO HIM. HE'S JUST USING HER TO GET AT ME. ONCE SHE'S SERVED HIS PURPOSE HE'LL KILL HER WITHOUT A SECOND THOUGHT.

*SEE "MARKED FOR MURDER," DD #159 -- JO.

THIS HAS BECOME A GAME TO HIM. A SICK LITTLE GAME OF RE-VENGE. HE WANTS ME TO FIND HIM.

AND, SO HELP ME, HE WON'T BE DIS-APPOINTED. I'LL SCOUR EVERY UNDER-WORLD DIVE IN THIS CITY UNTIL I DO!

BAR JOSIE'S GRILL

WELL, WELL... "LARK" LOGAN. GOT A MINUTE TO SING FOR YOUR SUPPER, STOOLIE?

THEY'RE SQUARING OFF IN THE CENTER OF THE RING!

MISTER, I GOT ALL THE TIME IN THE WORLD--

--BUT NOT FOR YOU OR YOUR INSULTS!

AND THERE'S THE BELL!

MAKE TIME, STOOLIE. I NEED ANSWERS.

SO? WHO DON'T?

WHAT CAN YOU TELL ME ABOUT A MAN CALLED BULLSEYE?

WHAT A STRUGGLE!

BULLSEYE, HUH? LET ME THINK...

YOU DO THAT, STOOLIE. THINK REAL HARD. I'M SURE SOMETHING WILL COME TO YOU.

HEY, MITHITHIPPI--!

YEAH...I'M BEGINNIN' TO SEE WHAT YOU MEAN!

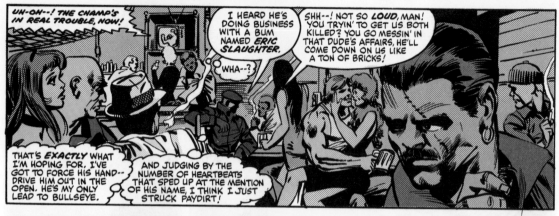

UH-OH--! THE CHAMP'S IN REAL TROUBLE, NOW!

I HEARD HE'S DOING BUSINESS WITH A BUM NAMED *ERIC SLAUGHTER.*

WHA--?

SHH--! NOT SO *LOUD,* MAN! YOU TRYIN' TO GET US BOTH KILLED? YOU GO MESSIN' IN THAT DUDE'S AFFAIRS, HE'LL COME DOWN ON US LIKE A TON OF BRICKS!

THAT'S *EXACTLY* WHAT I'M HOPING FOR, I'VE GOT TO FORCE HIS HAND-- DRIVE HIM OUT IN THE OPEN. HE'S MY ONLY LEAD TO BULLSEYE.

AND JUDGING BY THE NUMBER OF HEARTBEATS THAT SPED UP AT THE MENTION OF HIS NAME, I THINK I JUST STRUCK PAYDIRT!

PUTH THE DRINK DOWN, MITHER! NITHE AN' THLOW!

HELLO, TURK, HOW'S THE JAW?

I'M ONLY GONNA ASK YOU ONCE. WHAT DO YOU WANT WITH MR. SLAUGHTER?

NOTHING. I WANT BULLS-EYE.

AND I *DON'T* WANT NO TROUBLE WITH THE COPS, TURK! PUT THAT ROD AWAY-- *NOW!*

AW, JOTHIÉ...

OH, MOMMA--! WHAT A PUNCH!

KRAKK

YOU HEARD THE LADY!

AND, THE NEXT INSTANT...

WATCH OUT!

HEY! WHERE'D HE GO?

WHY, YOU LITTLE--!

I DUNNO! I NEVER SAW NO-BODY MOVE THAT FAST--

--EXCEPT...NAW, IT CAN'T BE! NOT HERE!

36

HERE HE IS! HURRY! HE FIGHTS LIKE A DEVIL!

THE GREAT BABBA'S USING EVERY DIRTY TRICK THERE IS!

IT'S TOTAL MAYHEM IN THE RING!

I GOT A NASTY FEELIN' ABOUT THIS!

JUTH THUT UP, DECKER, AN' FIND THAT GUY BEFORE--

SPAKK

--THE LIGHTH!

THAKK

THUMP

I KNEW IT! I JUST KNEW--

KRAKK

--IIIIT!

O-OH, NO--! LOOK! I-IT'S--!

IT'S TIME YOU LEARNED THE FACTS OF LIFE!

FACT: THERE'S A CONTRACT OUT FOR MY DEATH.

THUUP

FACT: I DON'T LIKE IT. I DON'T LIKE IT ONE BIT!

HOW MUCH DID BULLSEYE OFFER YOU TO KILL ME?

PLENTY, DEVIL!

KRAKK

MORE THAN YOU'RE WORTH, THAT'S FOR SURE!

NOW'S OUR CHANCE!

STICK 'IM!

NO, YOU DON'T HAVE A CHANCE.

YOU NEVER DID.

O-OH, DEAR--!

PROLOGUE

I WANT YOU TO FIND BULLSEYE, TURK. AND WHEN YOU DO, TELL HIM--

--DAREDEVIL IS COMING!

NEXT: FOR THE *LIFE* OF THE WIDOW, DAREDEVIL STALKS AN--

ISLAND OF DEATH!

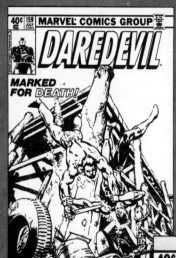

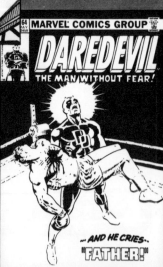

IT'TH **DAREDEVIL!** HE'TH ON TO UTH! HE EVEN KNOWTH ABOUT BULLTHEYE!

A-AN' HE THED HE'TH COMIN' AFTER **YOU** NEKTHT, MITHER THAUTHER!

YES, I SUSPECTED AS MUCH.

BUT APPARENTLY **YOU** DID NOT SUSPECT HE WOULD SIMPLY FOLLOW YOU HERE!

YOU ARE A FRIGHTENED LITTLE **FOOL,** TURK. I DO NOT LIKE FRIGHTENED LITTLE FOOLS.

KRAK

BETTER GO EASY ON YOUR HIRED HELP, SLAUGHTER. HURTING THEM'S NOT GOOD FOR BUSINESS.

MY BUSINESS, DAREDEVIL, IS **MURDER--**
--YOURS!

AND **MINE** IS FINDING BULLSEYE.

HE PUT OUT A CONTRACT FOR MY DEATH. ONE **YOU** WERE QUICK TO ACCEPT--

WELL, HE SUCCEEDED. I'M HERE, SLAUGHTER, AND I **WANT** HIM. I WANT HIM SO BADLY I CAN TASTE IT!

--AND PREDICTABLY SLOW TO FULFILL. WHEN YOU CAME UP EMPTY, HE **KIDNAPPED** THE BLACK WIDOW, INTENDING TO LEAD ME INTO SOME SORT OF TRAP.

43

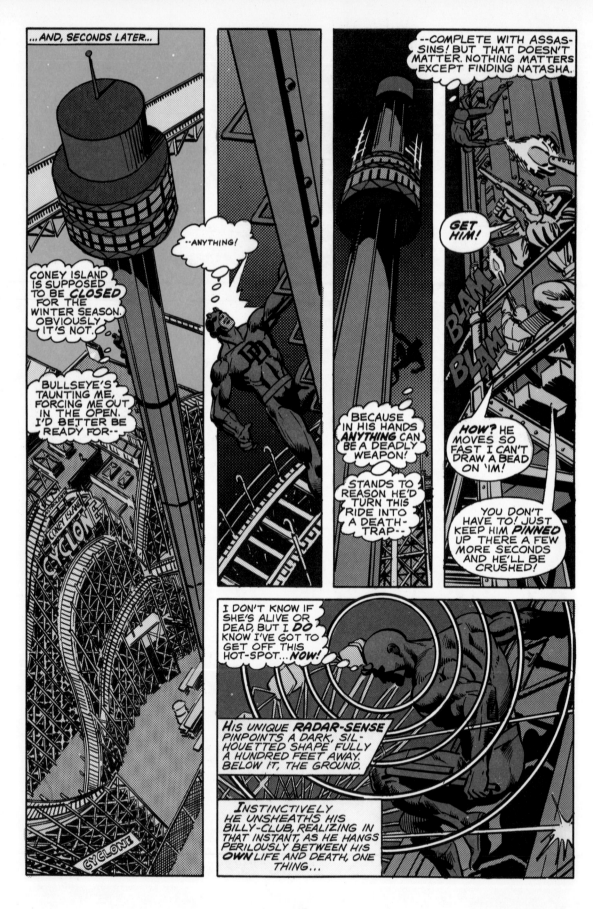

...AND, SECONDS LATER...

CONEY ISLAND IS SUPPOSED TO BE *CLOSED* FOR THE WINTER SEASON. OBVIOUSLY IT'S NOT.

BULLSEYE'S TAUNTING ME, FORCING ME OUT IN THE OPEN. I'D BETTER BE READY FOR--

--ANYTHING!

BECAUSE IN HIS HANDS *ANYTHING* CAN BE A DEADLY WEAPON!

STANDS TO REASON HE'D TURN THIS RIDE INTO A DEATH-TRAP--

--COMPLETE WITH ASSAS-SINS! BUT THAT DOESN'T MATTER. NOTHING MATTERS EXCEPT FINDING NATASHA.

GET HIM!

BLAM BLAM

HOW? HE MOVES SO FAST I CAN'T DRAW A BEAD ON 'IM!

YOU DON'T HAVE TO! JUST KEEP HIM *PINNED* UP THERE A FEW MORE SECONDS AND HE'LL BE CRUSHED!

I DON'T KNOW IF SHE'S ALIVE OR DEAD, BUT I *DO* KNOW I'VE GOT TO GET OFF THIS HOT-SPOT... *NOW!*

HIS UNIQUE *RADAR-SENSE* PINPOINTS A DARK, SIL-HOUETTED SHAPE FULLY A HUNDRED FEET AWAY. BELOW IT, THE GROUND.

INSTINCTIVELY HE UNSHEATHS HIS BILLY-CLUB, REALIZING IN THAT INSTANT, AS HE HANGS PERILOUSLY BETWEEN HIS *OWN* LIFE AND DEATH, ONE THING...

...IT IS AN *IMPOSSIBLE* JUMP!

KDAK

AND TO DARE THE IMPOSSIBLE, A MAN MUST EITHER BE *BLIND*...

THAPP

...OR *FEARLESS*.

OR BOTH.

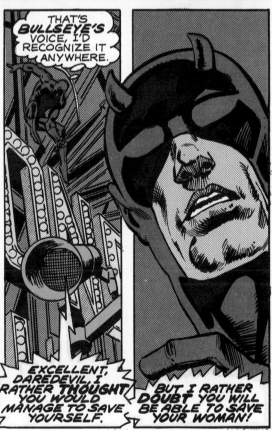

THAT'S *BULLSEYE'S* VOICE, I'D RECOGNIZE IT ANYWHERE.

EXCELLENT, DAREDEVIL, I RATHER THOUGHT YOU WOULD MANAGE TO SAVE YOURSELF.

BUT I RATHER *DOUBT* YOU WILL BE ABLE TO SAVE YOUR *WOMAN!*

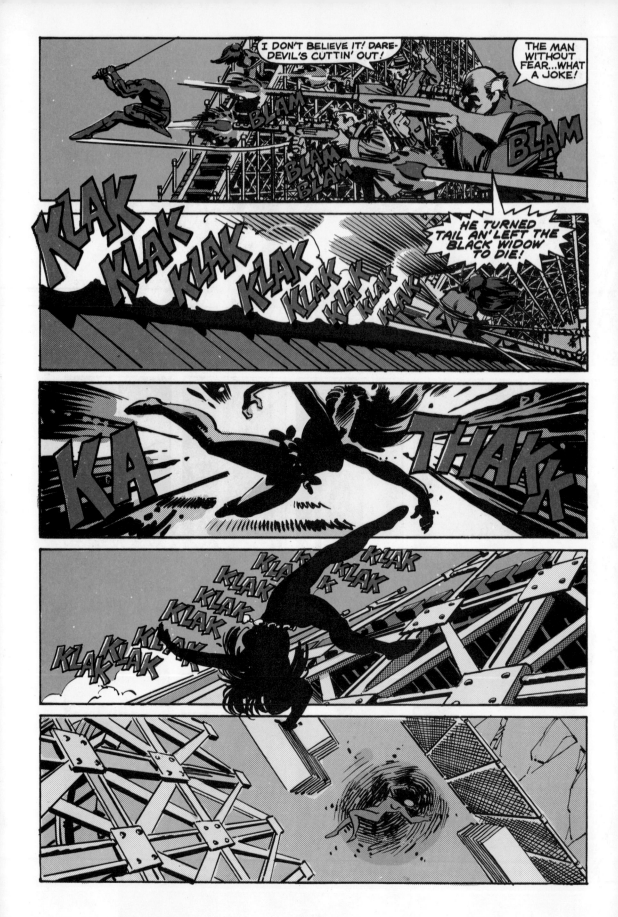

AND, IN THE ARCADE...

HE KNEW! SOME-HOW...SOME WAY... HE KNEW!

BUT THAT DOESN'T CHANGE A THING.

I STILL HAVE *YOU,* WIDOW. YOU ARE THE FLAME--

--AND DARE-DEVIL IS THE MOTH, DRAWN TO THE FLAME.

HE WILL *FIND* YOU, SOONER OR LATER--

--OR WHAT'S LEFT OF YOU--

--AN' WHEN HE DOES, WE'LL *BURN* 'IM!

YOU'RE INSANE! *ALL* OF YOU!

THAT, WIDOW, IS A MOOT POINT.

THOK

49

POINT IS, MR. URICH, YOU'S THE FIRST *REPORTER* I SEEN 'ROUND HERE SINCE BATTLIN' JACK MURDOCK WAS MURDERED, YEARS AGO.

I S'POSE MOST FOLKS DONE FORGOT ALL ABOUT IT, NOW, BUT I AIN'T.

JACK WAS A GOOD BOXER AN' A GOOD FRIEND.

K.O., DID HE EVER SAY JUST WHY HE DECIDED TO SIGN ROSCOE SWEENY AS HIS MANAGER?

YOU MEAN *THE FIXER*--? I TOLE JACK HE WAS MAKIN' A BIG MISTAKE, DEALIN' WITH THAT UNDERWORLD SCUM.

BUT JACK WAS GITTIN' OLD, AN' BOXIN' WAS ALL HE KNOWED. SO HE HAD TO KEEP ON FIGHTIN'... EVEN IF IT MEANT DEALIN' WITH SWEENY.

JACK FIGGERED HE OWED IT TO HIS SON. BUT WHEN HE WOULDN'T TAKE A DIVE, THE FIXER HAD 'IM GUNNED DOWN LIKE A DOG IN THE STREET.

SAY, LOUIE, WHAT'D THAT REPORTER WANT?

I DUNNO. HE WAS ASKIN' ME A LOTA' QUESTIONS 'BOUT SOME PUG NAMED MURDOCK.

SO I TOLD 'IM TO CHECK WID K.O.! THAT OLD PUSH-BROOM'S BEEN HANGIN' 'ROUND HERE FOR YEARS...

YOU MENTIONED MURDOCK'S SON. THAT WOULD BE *MATTHEW*, RIGHT?

YEAH, HE'S A CRACKER-JACK LAWYER NOW. JACK WOULDA BEEN PROUD.

HE WAS ALWAYS TELLIN' MATT TO STUDY AN' MAKE SOMETHIN' OF HISSELF.

'COURSE MATT WAS A BIT OF A LONER EVEN *BEFORE* HE LOST HIS EYE-SIGHT. A REAL BOOK-WORM. NEIGHBORHOOD KIDS USED T'TEASE 'IM... EVEN MADE UP A NICKNAME FOR 'IM. NOW, WHAT WAS IT...?

DAREDEVIL?

HOW DID *YOU* KNOW THAT?

JUST A HUNCH, K.O., JUST A HUNCH...

ONE THAT HAS SUPPLIED YET *ANOTHER* FACT TO WHAT WILL UNDOUBTEDLY PROVE THE MOST SENSATIONAL STORY OF BEN URICH'S TWENTY-YEAR JOURNALISTIC CAREER...

AND, BACK AT CONEY ISLAND...

DARE-DEVIL!

OH, NO--!

I WANT BULLSEYE, TURK. I WANT HIM NOW.

EITHER YOU TELL ME WHERE HE IS, OR THIS TIME I'LL BREAK *MORE* THAN YOUR JAW.

TH-THURE... WHATEVER YOU THAY! HE'TH IN THE ARCADE!

ONLY... *PLEATHE...* DON'T DROP ME!

DON'T PLAY GAMES, CUTTER, JUST GET IT OVER WITH.

I WANT HER DEAD BEFORE DAREDEVIL GETS HERE.

THEY THINK I'M HELPLESS.

THOK

BUT...I'M THE... BLACK WIDOW.

THOK

HOLD IT, YOU FOOL! CAN'T YOU SEE WHAT SHE'S DOING?

I'M... NEVER... HELP- LESS.

SNAKK

YOU USED ME, BULLSEYE. YOU USED ME, AND YOU HUMILIATED ME...

...AND YOU TRIED TO PUSH ME TO THE BREAKING POINT.

I DON'T LIKE THAT.

I DON'T LIKE YOUR HIRED MUSCLE.

AND I DON'T LIKE YOU.

YOUR LIKES AND DISLIKES ARE NO CONCERN OF MINE, WIDOW.

BUT YOUR *DEATH* IS. YOURS, AND MOST ESPECIALLY DAREDEV--!

THAPP

53

54

THE SCENT OF GUNPOWDER, THE CLICK OF A HAMMER... BULLSEYE HAS A GUN!

AND, ACCORDING TO MY RADAR-SENSE, HE'S BETWEEN ME AND MY BILLY CLUB. I'LL HAVE TO FACE THE WORLD'S DEADLIEST SHOT BAREHANDED!

I HAD HIM T-TRAPPED... BEATEN...W-WHY DIDN'T HE GIVE UP? WHAT... WHAT SORT OF MAN *IS* HE?

NO, DEVIL! I'M *NOT* FINISHED YET!

BUT HIS HEART'S POUNDING...

...HIS HAND'S SHAKING SO BADLY HE CAN BARELY HOLD THAT REVOLVER.

I MIGHT JUST BE ABLE TO RUN A *BLUFF*...

YOU TRIED THAT BEFORE, REMEMBER?

AREN'T YOU? THEN GO AHEAD, SHOOT.

IT DIDN'T STOP ME THEN. AND IT WON'T STOP ME NOW.

NOTHING YOU CAN DO WILL STOP ME NOW.

N-NO!

SLAUGHTER, DON'T JUST STAND THERE, YOU FOOL! I-- I'LL DOUBLE OUR CONTRACT, JUST KILL DAREDEVIL!

KILL HIM!

DOUBLE THE--?! JUTH THAY THE WORD, MITHER THAUTHER, AN' WE'LL BLOW 'EM AWAY!

NO! DAREDEVIL HAS EARNED MY RESPECT. BULLSEYE, ON THE OTHER HAND, HAS NOT. BESIDES, I DO NOT TRUST A *MAD-MAN* TO MEET HIS... AH... FINANCIAL COMMITMENTS.

BULLSEYE, LISTEN TO ME. IF YOU WANT DAREDEVIL DEAD, *YOU* KILL HIM.

YOU THINK I WON'T? WELL, I'LL SHOW YOU! I'LL SHOW YOU ALL!

Y-YOU'RE ALL AGAINST ME, AREN'T YOU? YES, I SEE, NOW!

BUT THAT DOESN'T MATTER. I'M BULLS-EYE...HEHHEH...AND IN MY HANDS...HEHHEH ...MY HANDS...

...D-DON'T HURT ME... DEVIL... HEHHEH...

...D-DEVIL...

DAREDEVIL, HIS MIND--

IT'S OVER, NATASHA. COME ON, WE'RE GETTING OUT OF HERE.

...DEVIL...

AND NO ONE'S GOING TO STOP US.

WE'LL MEET AGAIN, DAREDEVIL. THINGS WILL BE DIFFERENT, THEN.

COUNT ON IT, SLAUGH-TER.

COUNT ON IT.

NEXT ISSUE **BLIND ALLEY** --A CLASSIC CONFRONTATION BETWEEN MAN AND MONSTER AS DAREDEVIL FACES **THE HULK!** YOU DARE NOT MISS IT.

PRESENTING A MIGHTY MARVEL BONUS PAGE-- THE *SECRETS* OF DAREDEVIL'S BILLY CLUB!

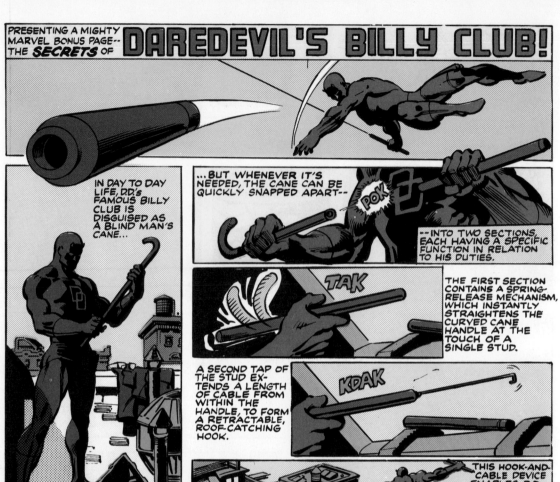

IN DAY TO DAY LIFE, D.D.'s FAMOUS BILLY CLUB IS DISGUISED AS A BLIND MAN'S CANE...

...BUT WHENEVER IT'S NEEDED, THE CANE CAN BE QUICKLY SNAPPED APART--

POK

--INTO TWO SECTIONS, EACH HAVING A SPECIFIC FUNCTION IN RELATION TO HIS DUTIES.

TAK

THE FIRST SECTION CONTAINS A SPRING-RELEASE MECHANISM, WHICH INSTANTLY STRAIGHTENS THE CURVED CANE HANDLE AT THE TOUCH OF A SINGLE STUD.

A SECOND TAP OF THE STUD EXTENDS A LENGTH OF CABLE FROM WITHIN THE HANDLE, TO FORM A RETRACTABLE, ROOF-CATCHING HOOK.

KDAK

THIS HOOK-AND-CABLE DEVICE ENABLES D.D. TO SWING ACROSS DISTANCES TOO GREAT FOR HIM TO LEAP.

THE STRAIGHTENED CANE HANDLE CAN REVERT TO ITS CURVED SHAPE WHEN HORNHEAD NEEDS TO HOLD ONTO A LEDGE OR CARRY ADDED WEIGHT.

THOK!

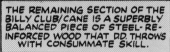

THE REMAINING SECTION OF THE BILLY CLUB/CANE IS A SUPERBLY BALANCED PIECE OF STEEL-REINFORCED WOOD THAT D.D. THROWS WITH CONSUMMATE SKILL.

D.D.'s COSTUME FEATURES A LEG-HOLSTER, IN WHICH HE STORES BOTH SECTIONS OF THIS ELEGANT WEAPON.

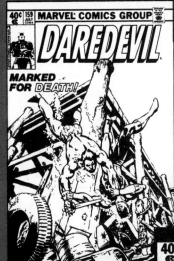

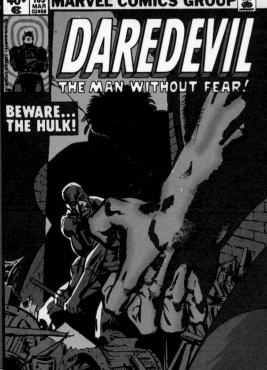

He dwells in eternal night—but the blackness is filled with sounds and scents other men cannot perceive. Though attorney MATT MURDOCK is *blind*, his other senses function with *superhuman sharpness*—his *radar sense* guides him over every obstacle! He stalks the streets by night, a red-garbed foe of evil!

STan Lee PRESENTS: DAREDEVIL, THE MAN WITHOUT FEAR!™

THE OCCASION IS A HUNDRED DOLLAR A PLATE FUNDRAISER, LAUNCHING THE RE-ELECTION CAMPAIGN OF DISTRICT ATTORNEY BLAKE TOWER.

Monster Sighted in Manhattan

A green behemoth may be hiding somewhere in New York City. State and local police to...ers early...the crea...as the...een in the...town...

BUT THE MAIN TOPIC OF CONVERSATION THIS EVENING CENTERS AROUND A MISUNDERSTOOD MAN-MONSTER...

THE HULK IS A UNIQUE CASE, JUDGE COFFIN. I DON'T BELIEVE FORCE WILL SOLVE THE PROBLEM.

FORCE IS THE *ONLY* SOLUTION, TOWER!

THE BUGLE HAS ALWAYS BEEN PROGRESSIVE, STARK. MY PAPER WAS THE *FIRST* TO EXPOSE THE SPIDER-MAN MENACE.

HULK IN NY

FRANKLY, JAMESON, PRINTING, UNSUBSTANTIATED RUMORS STRIKES ME AS *IRRESPONSIBLE* JOURNALISM.

IRRE--?!

MURDOCK, YOU DEFENDED THE HULK ONCE.

WHAT DO YOU THINK?

I *DOUBT* ANY LAWYER WHO WOULD REPRESENT THAT BRUTE *CAN* THINK.

UH, MATT, I'M SURE HIS HONOR DIDN'T MEAN--!

DON'T BE RIDICULOUS, TOWER! I MEANT *EVERY* WORD!

...AND THEN THE PRIEST SAYS TO THE RABBI...

HELLO, MATTHEW.

HEATHER! HOW HAVE YOU BEEN?

NEVER BETTER, MATTHEW... SINCE I MET RICO. HE'S INTO DISCO, KNOWS ALL THE MOVES.

KNOW 'EM? ANGEL-FACE, I INVENTED MOST OF 'EM!

PUT 'ER THERE, SPORT!

EH--?

HEY, SPORT, I'M TALKIN' TO YOU!

THAT SOUNDS LIKE...

OH, NO!

MATTHEW MURDOCK, YOU COULD AT LEAST TRY TO ACT CIVIL!

I'VE GOT TO GET OUT OF HERE! THE NOISE AND CONFUSION ARE LIKE A BLANKET ON MY HYPER-SENSES...

...BUT IF WHAT I SUSPECT IS TRUE...

WELL, I LIKE THAT!

MS. GLENN, I THINK YOUR EX-BOYFRIEND HAS JUST GIVEN US THE SNUB!

UH, PARDON ME, FATHER!

MR. NELSON, IT WILL BE MY PLEASURE!

MATT'S BEEN MOPING AROUND EVER SINCE HEATHER LEFT HIM.

A DOSE OF THE PATENTED NELSON CHARM OUGHT TO SNAP HIM OUT OF HIS FUNK, THOUGH.

THAT DISTINCTIVE, FRENETIC HEARTBEAT... LOUD AS A JACKHAMMER, EVEN BLOCKS AWAY! THERE'S NO DOUBT--

-- THE HULK IS LOOSE IN NEW YORK!

HE'S PROBABLY CONFUSED, CERTAINLY DANGEROUS. I--!

MATT, YOU OLD HOUND DOG, I KNOW HOW YOU MUST FEEL, BUT EVERYTHING WILL WORK OUT FOR THE BEST.

I MEAN, YOU AND HEATHER STILL LOVE EACH OTHER, RIGHT?

MATT, I'M YOUR BEST FRIEND. CAN'T YOU CONFIDE IN ME?

I WISH I COULD, FOGGY...

IF THERE'S ANYTHING I CAN DO...

I COULD USE A GOOD, STIFF DRINK.

AND A LITTLE PRIVACY.

YOU GOT IT, PARTNER. AND, MATT, IF I WERE YOU...

61

...I WOULDN'T LET THIS GET ME DOWN!

MATT?

AND, AS FOGGY RETURNS TO THE TERRACE...

MATT... ...WHERE'D YOU GO?

ONCE AGAIN, BLIND ATTORNEY MATT MURDOCK HAS BEEN FORCED TO PUT HIS PERSONAL PROBLEMS ASIDE -- TO RACE WITH THE SPEED AND AGILITY OF A *DARE-DEVIL*...

...DOWN DARK, LITTER-STREWN BACKSTREETS, AS HIS UNIQUE RADAR-SENSE GUIDES HIM UNERRINGLY ALONG A TRAIL OF WANTON DESTRUCTION.

...UNTIL, AT LAST...

I'VE FOUND HIM!

THE HULK! I'D ALMOST FORGOTTEN HOW BIG HE IS!

IT'S INCREDIBLE... THAT GAMMA RADIATION MUTATED DR. ROBERT BRUCE BANNER INTO THE MOST TRAGIC.... UNPREDICTABLE....AND POWERFUL CREATURE TO EVER WALK THE FACE OF THE EARTH!

THUMP THUMP

THUMP THUMP

SOMEWAY, I HAVE TO REACH THE MAN INSIDE THE MONSTER... BEFORE IT'S TOO LATE!

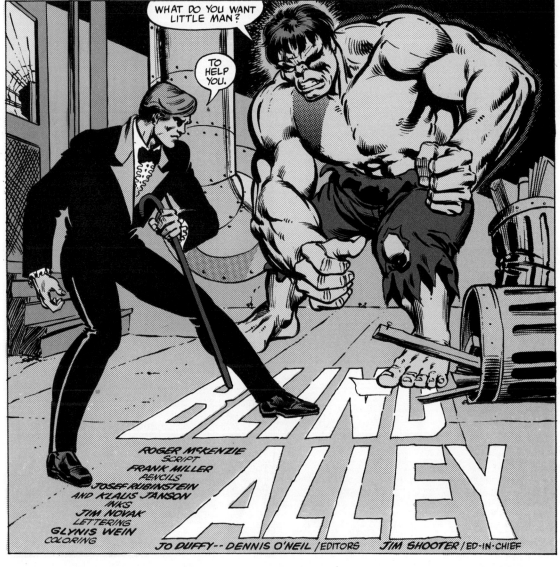

WHAT DO YOU WANT LITTLE MAN?

TO HELP YOU.

BLIND ALLEY

ROGER McKENZIE
SCRIPT
FRANK MILLER
PENCILS
JOSEF RUBINSTEIN
AND KLAUS JANSON
INKS
JIM NOVAK
LETTERING
GLYNIS WEIN
COLORING

JO DUFFY -- DENNIS O'NEIL / EDITORS   JIM SHOOTER / ED-IN-CHIEF

63

PLEASE, LISTEN TO ME: YOU CAN'T STAY HERE. IF I FOUND YOU, SO WILL OTHERS. THEY WILL COME WITH *GUNS* AND *TANKS* AND TRY TO *KILL* YOU.

THEY DON'T UNDERSTAND. THEY THINK YOU ARE A MONSTER.

I AM A MONSTER.

JUST LEAVE HULK ALONE, LITTLE MAN! HULK IS TIRED OF RUNNING!

HULK DOESN'T WANT YOUR HELP! HULK DOESN'T NEED YOUR HELP!

HULK DOESN'T NEED ANYONE'S HELP!

NOT EVEN BANNER'S?

64

HULK *HATES* BANNER, LITTLE MAN!

BANNER HURT HULK! BANNER *MADE* HULK A MONSTER!

WHERE IS BANNER, LITTLE MAN?

HULK, PLEASE, LISTEN TO REASON. YOU WON'T FIND BANNER THIS WAY. YOU *CAN'T* FIND BANNER THIS WAY.

VIOLENCE IS *NOT* THE ANSWER. I CAN HELP YOU FIND HIM, HULK, DO YOU UNDERSTAND? I CAN HELP YOU FIND BANNER, BUT YOU'LL HAVE TO *TRUST* ME.

THAT'S IT. RELAX. TRY TO THINK.

HULK DOESN'T WANT TO THINK, LITTLE MAN! HULK WANTS BANNER!

IT'S HARD FOR HULK TO THINK! IT HURTS HULK TO THINK! WHY DOES EVERYTHING HURT HULK?

WHY DID BANNER DO THIS TO HULK?

WHY DID...I ...DO THIS...

...TO... MYSELLLLFF

THE DARK AND SAVAGE SIDE OF DR. BANNER IS GONE. FOR NOW.

GONE, BUT NOT FORGOTTEN, EVEN HOURS LATER AT MATT MURDOCK'S UPPER EASTSIDE BROWNSTONE...

NO, HULK!

NOOOO!

THAT SAME NIGHT-MARE...OVER AND OVER AGAIN! I CAN'T ESCAPE THE HULK EVEN IN MY DREAMS!

BUT WHERE AM I? HOW--?

MORNING, BRUCE. HOPE YOU'RE FEELING BETTER

MATT? MATT MURDOCK?! IT'S BEEN YEARS, COUNSELLOR! BUT WHAT AM I DOING HERE?

DON'T YOU REMEMBER?

A LITTLE. MOSTLY I REMEMBER THE HATE...

A FEW MINUTES LATER...

...AND THE PAIN, THAT'S THE WORST PART, MATT. IT HURTS SO MUCH I...THE HULK JUST WANTS TO LASH OUT AT ANYONE OR ANYTHING THAT GETS IN MY WAY.

MORE COFFEE?

PLEASE. I MISS THINGS LIKE...WELL, LIKE A CUP OF COFFEE IN THE MORNING, I MISS LIVING A NORMAL LIFE.

MAYBE, WITH HELP, YOU COULD. THE AUTHORITIES...

NO!

HIS HEARTBEAT'S SPEEDING UP...HE'S GETTING UPSET...AND THAT TRIGGERS THE CHANGE IN HIM! I'VE GOT TO DO SOMETHING TO CALM HIM DOWN...AND FAST!

THE AUTHORITIES WON'T DEAL WITH ME, AND THEY CAN'T DEAL WITH WHAT I BECOME--

--WHEN...I...LOSE...CONTROL...

BUT YOU WON'T LOSE CONTROL, BRUCE, ANY MORE THAN I'D TURN YOU IN AGAINST YOUR WISHES. THINK ABOUT IT, BRUCE. I'M YOUR FRIEND...

Y-YES...MY FRIEND...

...AND ALL I WANT TO DO IS HELP YOU. IF YOU NEED MONEY, CLOTHES--

Y-YOU'VE DONE MORE THAN ENOUGH ALREADY, MATT. I COULDN'T ASK YOU TO--

BRUCE, PLEASE, FOR BOTH OUR SAKES, DON'T ARGUE WITH ME!

AND SO...

SO LONG, MATT. AND THANKS. THANKS FOR EVERYTHING.

GOODBYE, BRUCE. GOOD LUCK...

IT HELPED ME, TALKING TO MATT. I FEEL GOOD, AND I'LL FEEL EVEN BETTER ONCE I'M OUT OF NEW YORK.

IF SOMETHING SHOULD HAPPEN TO SEND THE HULK ON A RAMPAGE HERE--

--BUT NOTHING WILL HAPPEN. NOT IF I JUST TAKE IT EASY AND DO THIS BY THE NUMBERS. MY BEST BET IS TO TAKE THE SUBWAY TO PORT AUTHORITY, THEN GRAB THE FIRST GREYHOUND WEST.

THE HULK WAS CREATED THERE, IN THE DESERT, A TORTURED, UNCOMPREHENDING, AND AWESOMELY POWERFUL CHILD OF THE ATOM.

I DESIGNED THE GAMMA BOMB THAT ACCIDENTALLY GAVE HIM LIFE WHEN I WAS EXPOSED TO ITS RADIATION. SOMEDAY, I'LL FIND A WAY TO REVERSE THE PROCESS... TO GIVE HIM THE PEACE HE SO DESPERATELY CRAVES.

I WISH I COULD HANDLE MY HANDICAP AS WELL AS MATT HANDLES HIS. HE LOST HIS SIGHT, BUT BECAUSE OF THE HULK, I'VE LOST EVERYTHING. THE WOMAN I LOVE, MY CAREER...

EVEN MY HUMANITY.

BUT IF IT'S HUMANITY BRUCE WANTS, HE FINDS PLENTY AS THE #6 LOCAL SCREECHES TO A HALT, AND THE RUSH HOUR CROWD ELBOWS HIM ONTO AN ALREADY PACKED CAR.

THE TRIP DOWNTOWN SHOULD ONLY TAKE TWENTY MINUTES, TOPS.

BUT IT SEEMS A LIFETIME.

:KOFF:
:KOFF:

LET HULK *OUT* OF HERE!

BUT THE ONLY ANSWER HE GETS IS THE IMPATIENT SNARL OF CARS, BUSES AND CABS ALONG A SUDDENLY IMPASSABLE LEXINGTON AVENUE.

C'MON! MOVE IT UP THERE! TRAFFIC GETS WORSE EVERY DAY!

IT'S ENOUGH TO DRIVE A GUY CRAZY!

OH, NO! I CAN HEAR PEOPLE RUNNING, SHOUTING IN FEAR! AND THAT OVERPOWERING HEARTBEAT...

ALL BRUCE WANTED WAS A CHANCE TO GET SAFELY OUT OF NEW YORK, BUT HE OBVIOUSLY DIDN'T MAKE IT.

AND NEITHER DID THE HULK.

POK POK

QUICKLY PAYING HIS FARE, MATT SLIPS UNSEEN AND UNSEEING INTO THE SHADOWS OF A SPRAWLING METROPOLIS THAT HAS AWAKENED TO A NIGHTMARE.

TAK

THE MAN-CREATURE THAT MOMENTS AGO WAS DR. ROBERT BRUCE BANNER BELLOWS HIS DEMAND AT THE TOP OF HIS LUNGS... AND THE END OF HIS PATIENCE.

A RAMPAGING NIGHT-MARE CALLED--

THE HULK!

RUN!

WHAT DO YOU WANT, HULK?

BANNER! HULK WILL NOT LEAVE THE CITY UNTIL HULK FINDS BANNER!

...EVACUATE THE AREA! WE'LL NEED RIOT SQUADS, FIRETRUCKS, AND AMBU-LANCES!

YEAH, DARE-DEVIL'S HERE, BUT YOU'D BETTER CON-TACT THE AVENGERS, WHAT?! YOU CAN'T?! THEY AREN'T? AND THE FANTASTIC FOUR'S OUTTA TOWN, TOO?

YEAH, RIGHT. I'LL DO WHAT I CAN...

BANNER TORMENTS HULK, LITTLE MAN!

NO, YOU TOR-MENT YOURSELF. PLEASE, CALM DOWN BEFORE SOMEONE GETS HURT.

BLAMMM

SO, LITTLE MAN, YOU TRIED TO TRICK HULK! ALL YOU KNOW IS HOW TO HURT!

BUT HULK CAN HURT, TOO! YOU TAUGHT HULK HOW! BANNER TAUGHT HULK HOW, TOO! AND NOW HULK IS THROUGH RUNNING!

BLAM

BLAM

BLAM BLAM

BLAM

KLIK KLIK KLIK

OHHHHH...

N-NOTHING... I COULD...DO. HULK'S TOO STRONG...TOO BRUTAL. LUCKY...TO BE... ALIVE...

TRIED MY BEST ...TO STOP HULK. BEST WASN'T... GOOD ENOUGH.

IF I QUIT NOW, NOBODY WOULD BLAME ME...NOBODY WOULD EVEN KNOW...

NOBODY...EXCEPT ME. I'D ALWAYS KNOW THAT I'D BACKED DOWN... THAT I RAN...

HULK IS TIRED OF RUNNING!

HULK WILL STAY IN THIS CITY UNTIL HULK FINDS BANNER!

WHERE ARE YOU, BANNER?

YOU CAN'T HIDE FROM HULK FOREVER, BANNER! IF HULK HAS TO, HULK WILL DESTROY CITY! BUT HULK WILL FIND--

--YOU?!

RRROOM!

HUH! IT'S NOT BANNER! JUST A LITTLE MAN WHO TRIED TO HURT THE HULK WITH BIG MACHINE!

HULK HATES MACHINES!

BANNER TRIED TO HURT HULK WITH MACHINES!

HULK HATES BANNERRRR!

THE HULK'S GONE BERSERK! WHY DOESN'T DAREDEVIL CLEAR OUTTA THERE? WHAT SORT OF MAN *IS* HE TO DARE TO STAND UP TO THAT... THAT MONSTER?

HEY, LADY! GET BACK HERE!

SOMEBODY *STOP* THAT WOMAN!

MATT!

THAT'S HEATHER GLENN, MURDOCK'S GIRL! BUT WHAT DID SHE JUST SAY... MATT?!

FOR THE PAST TWENTY YEARS, BEN URICH HAS BEEN A DEPENDABLE, IF UNSPECTACULAR, REPORTER FOR THE DAILY BUGLE...

74

...BUT FOR THE PAST FEW WEEKS HE HAS BEEN CAREFULLY ASSEMBLING THE MYRIAD PIECES OF THE BIGGEST EXCLUSIVE OF HIS CAREER.

TODAY, WITH A SINGLE WORD, HIS JOURNALISTIC PUZZLE HAS BEEN COMPLETED.

LADY, IF THERE WAS ANYTHING I COULD DO, I'D BE DOIN' IT!

PLEASE...DO SOMETHING BEFORE THAT THING KILLS MA--!

HULK... ...IN THE NAME OF GOD... ...LISTEN TO REASON!

DESTROYING NEW YORK WON'T SOLVE ANYTHING!

YOU WON'T FIND BANNER THAT WAY!

YOU CAN'T FIND BANNER THAT WAY!

DON'T YOU UNDERSTAND?

YOU ARE BANNER!

NO!

BANNER MADE THE HULK A MONSTER AND HULK WILL FIND HIM, EVEN IF IT TAKES FOREVER!

FOR MAN AND MONSTER ALIKE, EVENTS COME FULL CIRCLE...

75

...RETURNING, IN THE END, TO THE BLIND ALLEY WHERE THEY BEGAN...

HULK...⧼KOFF⧽... YOU WON'T FIND BANNER...⧼KOFF⧽ ...THIS WAY.

YOU CAN'T...⧼KOFF⧽... FIND BANNER THIS WAY.

...AND...⧼KOFF⧽... I WANT TO HELP YOU.

...BUT YOU'LL HAVE TO TRUST ME

THE POLICE...THE AUTHORITIES... I-I WANT TO HELP THEM UNDERSTAND ...⧼KOFF⧽...

THEN DAREDEVIL STAGGERS BACKWARD. HIS CHEST BURNS AS IF IT'S ON FIRE AND AGONY BLURS HIS RADAR-SENSE.

THE WORLD SEEMS TO LURCH DRUNKENLY BENEATH HIM AND THE LAST THING HE SENSES...

...IS A DARK AND HULKING FIGURE, LOOMING OVER HIM LIKE THE SHADOW OF DEATH...

MEDIC!

OVER HERE! HURRY! DAREDEVIL'S HAVING TROUBLE BREATHING! I THINK HIS RIBS ARE BROKEN...HE'S IN SHOCK!

HE DIDN'T HAVE A CHANCE! NOT AGAINST THE HULK! BUT HE DIDN'T BACK DOWN, EITHER. HE LAID HIS LIFE ON THE LINE FOR THIS TOWN!

NO WONDER HE'S CALLED THE MAN WITHOUT FEAR!

ANYBODY SEE WHERE THE HULK WENT?

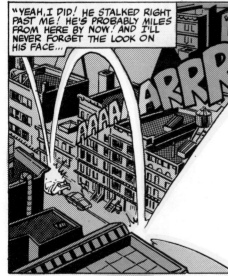

"YEAH, I DID! HE STALKED RIGHT PAST ME! HE'S PROBABLY MILES FROM HERE BY NOW! AND I'LL NEVER FORGET THE LOOK ON HIS FACE..."

"...LIKE HE'D JUST LOST HIS ONLY FRIEND..."

EPILOGUE

THE HOURS DRAG SLOWLY BY AS DAREDEVIL LIES IN BELLVIEW HOSPITAL'S INTENSIVE CARE UNIT, FIGHTING FOR HIS LIFE...

KLAK KLIK KLAK KLIK

...AND BEN URICH BENDS OVER HIS BATTERED TYPEWRITER, WRESTLING WITH A DEADLINE...

BEN, IT'S LATE. CAN'T THAT WAIT UNTIL TOMORROW?

NO, DARLING, IT CAN'T. YOU GO ON TO BED...

I WON'T BE LONG...

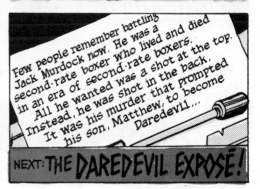

Few people remember battling Jack Murdock now. He was a second-rate boxer who lived and died in an era of second-rate boxers. All he wanted was a shot at the top. Instead, he was shot in the back. It was his murder that prompted his son, Matthew, to become Daredevil...

NEXT: THE DAREDEVIL EXPOSÉ!

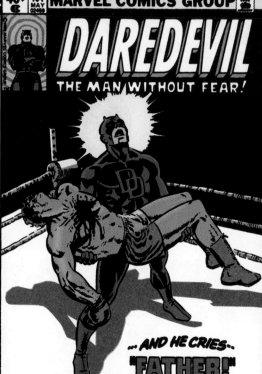

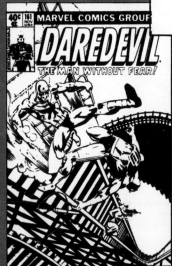

He dwells in eternal night—but the blackness is filled with sounds and scents other men cannot perceive. Though attorney MATT MURDOCK is *blind*, his other senses function with *superhuman sharpness*—his *radar sense* guides him over every obstacle! He stalks the streets by night, a red-garbed foe of evil!

STan Lee PRESENTS: DAREDEVIL, THE MAN WITHOUT FEAR!®

EXPOSÉ

NATASHA, IF THERE'S ANYTHING WE CAN DO...

DAILY BUGLE

DAREDEVIL BATTLES HULK

Man Without Fear Hospitalized — Condition

The mysterious, red-clad figure known as Daredevil was [...] to City Hospital early to-[...] a battle with the [...] en street.

According to witnesses Hulk escaped by bou[...] over rooftops in the di[...] of the Jersey shore.

The incident bega[...] sources say, when [...] encountered the H[...]

Roger McKenzie
WRITER

Frank Miller
ARTIST

Klaus Janson
INKER

John Costanza
LETTERER

Glynis Wein
COLORIST

Denny O'Neil
EDITOR

Jim Shooter - EDITOR-IN-CHIEF

YOU HEARD NURSE WILLOW, MISTER--?

URICH. BEN URICH. I'M A REPORTER FOR THE BUGLE AND I *HAVE* TO TALK TO DAREDEVIL... ALONE!

NO, YOU HAVE TO GET OUT OF HERE BEFORE--

IT'S OK, NATASHA. I KNOW BEN.

WELL, IF YOU'RE SURE IT'S ALL RIGHT...

AND, AFTER THE BLACK WIDOW AND NURSE WILLOW HAVE LEFT...

WHAT'S ON YOUR MIND, BEN?

A STORY, DARE-DEVIL. A VERY *SPECIAL* STORY... ABOUT YOU!

THAT'S AWFULLY FLATTERING, BEN, BUT MY CAREER IS PRETTY MUCH PUBLIC RECORD--

IT'S A BIT MORE *PERSONAL* THAN THAT. IT'S THE STORY OF A LONELY LITTLE BOY BLINDED BY A FREAK ACCIDENT.

AND IT'S THE STORY OF HOW HE OVERCAME HIS HANDICAP TO BECOME A SUCCESSFUL LAWYER *AND* A MAN WITHOUT FEAR.

IT'S *YOUR* STORY, MATTHEW MURDOCK, AND I CAN *PROVE* IT!

NOW JUST A MINUTE, BEN! YOU CAN'T SERIOUSLY BELIEVE I'M--

WELL, IF YOU'RE *NOT* MATT MURDOCK AND IF YOU'RE *NOT* BLIND, JUST DESCRIBE THIS PHOTOGRAPH TO ME AND I'LL LEAVE. I'LL FORGET THE WHOLE THING.

PHOTO--? BEN, I...I REALLY DON'T FEEL LIKE PLAYING GAMES.

I'M NOT MATT MURDOCK, I'M *CERTAINLY* NOT BLIND--

--AND I DON'T SEE WHY I HAVE TO PROVE *ANY-THING* TO YOU.

IT'S NONE OF YOUR BUSINESS... WHO I AM.

IT'S...

...IT'S...

...IT'S *TRUE*...

AND THIS MAN, *"BATTLIN"* JACK MURDOCK--?

DAD. HE WAS THE GREATEST.

I REMEMBER...

BUT I WANT TO GO OUT AND PLAY NOW, POP! I CAN STUDY LATER!

NO, MATT, YOUR HOME-WORK COMES FIRST. I *PROMISED* YOUR MOMMA BEFORE SHE... BEFORE SHE DIED...THAT I WOULDN'T LET YOU GROW UP TO BE AN UNEDUCATED PUG LIKE ME.

NOW *YOU* HAVE TO PROMISE ME SOMETHING, SON. PROMISE ME YOU'LL STUDY EVERY CHANCE YOU GET, THAT YOU'LL BECOME A DOCTOR OR A LAWYER...SOMEBODY IMPORTANT! PROMISE ME YOU'LL BE SOMEBODY *I* NEVER COULD...

I PROMISE, POP! YOU'LL BE PROUD OF ME! YOU'LL SEE...

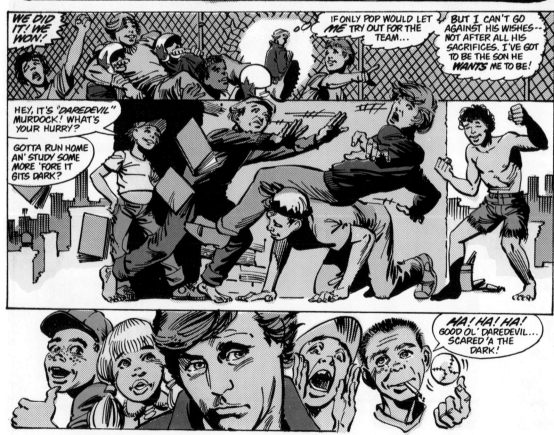

WE DID IT! WE WON!

IF ONLY POP WOULD LET *ME* TRY OUT FOR THE TEAM...

BUT I CAN'T GO AGAINST HIS WISHES-- NOT AFTER ALL HIS SACRIFICES. I'VE GOT TO BE THE SON HE *WANTS* ME TO BE!

HEY, IT'S *"DAREDEVIL"* MURDOCK! WHAT'S YOUR HURRY?

GOTTA RUN HOME AN' STUDY SOME MORE 'FORE IT GITS DARK?

HA! HA! HA! GOOD OL' DAREDEVIL... SCARED 'A THE DARK!

"IT WASN'T EASY, BEN, GROWING UP IN HELL'S KITCHEN, THE ONLY SON OF BATTLIN' MURDOCK. I GUESS EVERYONE JUST SORT OF EXPECTED ME TO BE A FIGHTER, TOO...

THEY LAUGHED AT ME! THEY THINK I'M A COWARD, BUT SOMEDAY I'LL SHOW THEM HOW WRONG THEY ARE! I--HEY!

THAT'S AN IDEA--! WHY DON'T I DO THIS EVERY DAY,... JUST TO KEEP IN SHAPE?!

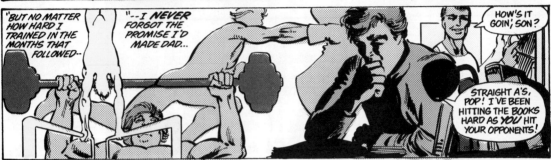

"BUT NO MATTER HOW HARD I TRAINED IN THE MONTHS THAT FOLLOWED--

"--I NEVER FORGOT THE PROMISE I'D MADE DAD...

HOW'S IT GOIN', SON?

STRAIGHT A'S, POP! I'VE BEEN HITTING THE BOOKS HARD AS YOU HIT YOUR OPPONENTS!

"BUT LATER I LEARNED DAD WASN'T HITTING MUCH OF ANYTHING...

...EXCEPT THE SKIDS...

JACK, I'M YOUR FRIEND AN' I'M BEGGIN' YA TO STEAR CLEAR 'A SWEENEY! YOU KNOW THAT CROOK'S REP AS A MANAGER!

ALL I KNOW IS BOXIN', KO, AND I HAVEN'T LANDED A FIGHT IN WEEKS!

JUST LOOKIT ME! I'M GETTIN' OLD AND I'M GETTIN' SLOW. I'M A HAS-BEEN. WE BOTH KNOW THAT.

AIN'T NO LEGIT MANAGER WILLIN' TO TAKE A CHANCE ON ME ANYMORE, BUT I GOTTA KEEP ON FIGHTIN' 'TILL MATT FINISHES COLLEGE!

I OWE HIM THAT...

I DON'T OWE YOU A THING, MURDOCK!

I TOLD YOU TEN YEARS AGO YOU'D COME CRAWLIN' TO ME ON YOUR KNEES ONE DAY!

HE'S A BUM, FIXER. ALWAYS BEEN A BUM, IF YOU ASK ME!

JACKIE BOY HERE COULD BE THE NEXT HEAVYWEIGHT CHAMPEEN...

WELL, I DIDN'T, SLADE, SO KEEP YOUR TRAP SHUT!

... WITH THE RIGHT MANAGER, OF COURSE!

HOW'S ABOUT IT, JACKIE BOY? YOU READY TO SIGN WITH THE FIXER?

I'M READY.

NOT SO FAST, JACKIE BOY.

"SWEENEY WAS NOTHING BUT TRASH, BEN."

"JUST LIKE THE RADIOACTIVE GUNK THE ARMY USED TO TRANSPORT THROUGH NEW YORK AT THE TIME."

"THEY HAD PREPARED FOR EVERY POSSIBLE CONTINGENCY."

"EXCEPT ONE.

MY RECRUITER DIDN'T TELL ME I'D BE RIDIN' HERD ON NO *ATOMIC BOMB!*

IT AIN'T A BOMB... ONLY THE STUFF THAT GOES INSIDE...

H-HEY!

WHAT'S WRONG, SARGE?

I...DUNNO. BAD CRAMP IN MY CHEST...

I CAN'T... *BREATHE--!*

IT HURTS!

"I REMEMBER WATCHING IN HORROR AS THE TRUCK SKIDDED OUT OF CONTROL TOWARD A HELPLESS OLD BLIND MAN."

GOTTA... *KOFF*... GET THIS CANNISTER... *KOFF*... AWAY FROM THE FLAMES--OR IT'LL *BLOW*--!

"THE NEXT THING I KNEW I WAS LYING IN THE STREET. I HEARD SOMETHING HEAVY SHATTER RIGHT BESIDE ME...

"...AND WHEN I LOOKED UP...

"I LOOKED INTO THE HEART OF A MAN-MADE SUN.

"IT WAS THE LAST THING I EVER SAW.

"I WOKE TO A HOSPITAL... AND DAD--"

SON, THAT WAS A BRAVE THING YOU DID. I JUST HOPE... SOMEDAY... I CAN MAKE YOU AS *PROUD* OF ME AS I AM OF YOU...

"MY REHABILITATION WAS A SLOW, PAINFUL, AND AT TIMES FRUSTRATING ORDEAL. I DON'T THINK I COULD HAVE MADE IT WITHOUT THE LOVE AND SUPPORT OF PEOPLE LIKE DAD--"

"--OR MY COLLEGE ROOMIE, FOGGY NELSON. THEY NEVER LET ME DOWN. NOT ONCE."

MATT, YOU OL' HOUND DOG, HOW DO YOU DO IT? I STUDY LIKE A DEMON, BUT *YOU* JUST BREEZE ALONG WITH TOP GRADES!

"AND, BEN, BECAUSE OF THE ACCIDENT, I WAS MORE DETERMINED THEN *EVER* TO GET MY LAW DEGREE. TO PROVE I COULD *STILL* BE A HUMAN BEING... DESPITE MY HANDICAP."

POP DESERVES THE CREDIT, FOGGY. HE HAD ME STUDY SO HARD WHEN I WAS YOUNGER THAT IT ALL SEEMS TO COME *EASY* FOR ME NOW.

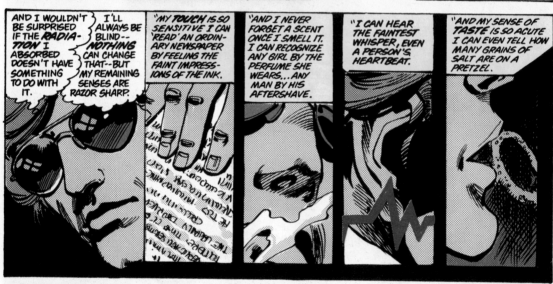

AND I WOULDN'T BE SURPRISED IF THE *RADIATION* I ABSORBED DOESN'T HAVE SOMETHING TO DO WITH IT.

I'LL ALWAYS BE BLIND-- *NOTHING* CAN CHANGE THAT--BUT MY REMAINING SENSES ARE RAZOR SHARP.

"MY *TOUCH* IS SO SENSITIVE I CAN 'READ' AN ORDINARY NEWSPAPER BY FEELING THE FAINT IMPRESSIONS OF THE INK."

"AND I NEVER FORGET A SCENT ONCE I SMELL IT. I CAN RECOGNIZE ANY GIRL BY THE PERFUME SHE WEARS...ANY MAN BY HIS AFTERSHAVE."

"I CAN HEAR THE FAINTEST WHISPER, EVEN A PERSON'S HEARTBEAT."

"AND MY SENSE OF *TASTE* IS SO ACUTE I CAN EVEN TELL HOW MANY GRAINS OF SALT ARE ON A PRETZEL."

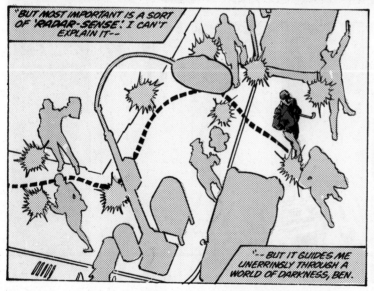

"BUT MOST IMPORTANT IS A SORT OF 'RADAR-SENSE.' I CAN'T EXPLAIN IT--"

"--BUT IT GUIDES ME UNERRINGLY THROUGH A WORLD OF DARKNESS, BEN."

SAY, SON... WANT ANY *HELP* CROSSING THE STREET?

NO THANKS, I CAN MAKE IT.

BUT, MATT, *WHY* DID YOU BECOME DAREDEVIL?

I THINK YOU ALREADY *KNOW* THE ANSWER TO THAT, BEN.

JUSTICE.

BLIND JUSTICE.

"WHILE I WAS FINISHING MY SCHOOLING, DAD'S CAREER WAS TAKING A SURPRISING TURN...

MURDOCK UPSETS SIMS

MURDOCK K.O.'S GAL IN SEVE

MIDDLE-AGED SENSATIO KES 10TH STRAIG

JACKIE BOY, YOU BEEN WORKIN' TOO HARD. YOU OUGHT'A TAKE IT EASY. REAL EASY.

SO EASY YOU *LOSE* YOUR NEXT FIGHT, KNOW WHAT I MEAN?

WHY, YOU LOUSY LITTLE--! I *NEVER* THREW A FIGHT IN MY LIFE!

I SURE AS HELL AIN'T GONNA START NOW!

JACKIE BOY, YOU EITHER TAKE A DIVE...

...OR YOU'RE A *DEAD* MAN!

MAN, OH, MAN! LISTEN TO THIS, MATT! IT SAYS IN THE PAPERS YOUR FATHER JUST SIGNED TO FIGHT ROCKY DAVIS AT THE GARDEN NEXT MONTH-- --AND THE WINNER'S *GUARANTEED* A SHOT AT THE CHAMP! WANNA GO?

SHOWDOWN AT THE GARDEN! BATTLIN' MURDOCK

FOGGY, I WOULDN'T *MISS* IT FOR THE WORLD!

"MADISON SQUARE GARDEN WAS *PACKED* THAT NIGHT, BEN.

DING!

"AND IF THE CROWD EXPECTED A *BLOODBATH*...

"...THEY WEREN'T *DISAPPOINTED.*"

GIT 'IM, MURDOCK!

ROCKYYY! ROCKYYY!

YOU'RE *NOTHIN'* OLD MAN!

YOU BEEN A *NOTHIN'* ALL YOUR LIFE!

AN' YOU'LL GO ON BEIN' A *NOTHIN'* OLD MAN...

...TILL THE DAY YOU *DIE!*

88

THIS ONE'S FOR *YOU*, MATT!

"DAD *WON* THE FIGHT.

BLAM

"BUT HE *LOST* HIS *LIFE*...

THIS ONE'S FOR *YOU*, BUM!

EASY, SON--

--THERE'S NOTHIN' YOU CAN DO, MATT. CAN'T *NOBODY* DO NOTHIN'!

HELL, MATT, YOU THINK I DON'T KNOW HOW YOU FEEL? YOU THINK *I* DON'T HURT, TOO?

JACK AN' ME, WE WENT BACK A LONG WAYS.

I *TOLD* 'IM NOT TO MESS WITH SWEENEY.

I'M TELLIN' *YOU* THE SAME THING. SWEENEY'S A *KILLER*, MATT.

JUST GIVE IT UP.

POP *NEVER* GAVE UP, KO.

NEITHER WILL I.

96